The Incredible Scotland Activity Book™

Editors: Nick Pierce, Caroline Coleman
Editorial assistant: Rob Walker

Published in Great Britain in MMXV by
Book House, an imprint of
The Salariya Book Company Ltd
25 Marlborough Place, Brighton BN1 1UB
www.salariya.com

PB ISBN-13: 978-1-910184-97-4

3 5 7 9 8 6 4 2

A CIP catalogue record for this book is available
from the British Library.
Printed and bound in China.
Printed on paper from sustainable sources.
Reprinted in MMXVII.

The Incredible Scotland Activity Book™

by Fiona Macdonald

illustrated by David Antram

Packed with facts and games!

BOOK HOUSE
a SALARIYA *imprint*

Join the dots
to meet Doodle
McDoodle.

Fàilte! (Welcome!)

Untangle the lines to help the tourists reach their destinations.

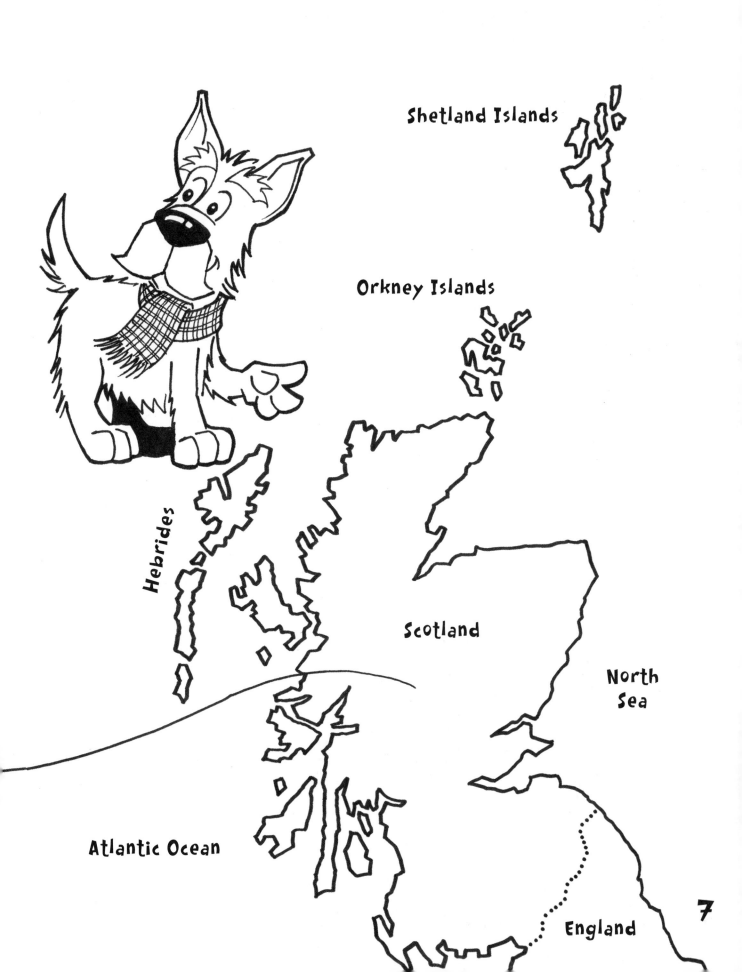

Shetland Islands

Orkney Islands

Hebrides

Scotland

North
Sea

Atlantic Ocean

England

7

Wordsearch

Find these Scottish cities and towns in the word search.

Aberdeen

Dumfries

Dundee

Glasgow

Stirling

Elgin

Perth

Edinburgh

I belong to Glasgow...

P	A	B	E	R	D	E	E	N	A
U	B	E	H	U	U	L	D	W	A	G
M	C	R	A	T	N	G	I	Y	F
F	V	W	D	B	D	I	N	E	G
R	C	I	S	D	E	N	B	I	L
I	E	C	P	G	E	H	U	J	A
E	R	K	E	F	T	L	R	K	S
S	T	I	R	L	I	N	G	S	G
I	Q	P	T	L	O	M	H	N	O
J	N	M	H	K	P	O	Q	R	W

Land Of Mists

Match the numbers on the map to the famous Scottish landmarks.

Old Man Of Hoy

2

7

6

1

9

Loch Lomond

3

5

8

4

River Clyde

Cairngorms

Fingal's Cave

Loch Ness

Rannoch Moor

Ben Nevis

Arthur's Seat

Mountain climbing

Help Doodle McDoodle's friend climb down the Mountain!

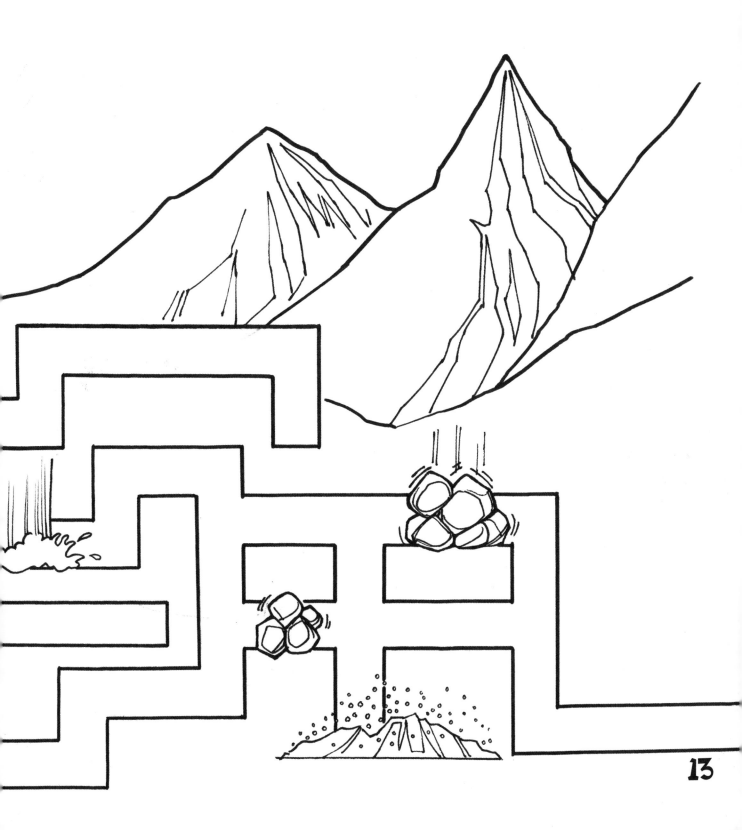

Crossword

Complete the crossword with the names of these famous Scots.

Mary, Queen of Scots
Monarch

James Simpson
Pioneered anaesthetics

David Livingstone
Explorer

Mary Slessor
Humanitarian

Joseph Lister
Pioneered antiseptics

Robert Louis Stevenson
Writer

Bonnie Prince Charlie
Would-be king

my heroes

Saint Columba
Missionary, traveller,
~ught Loch Ness Monster
(see p.40)

LandMarks

Match the shapes to the famous
constructions on the Map.

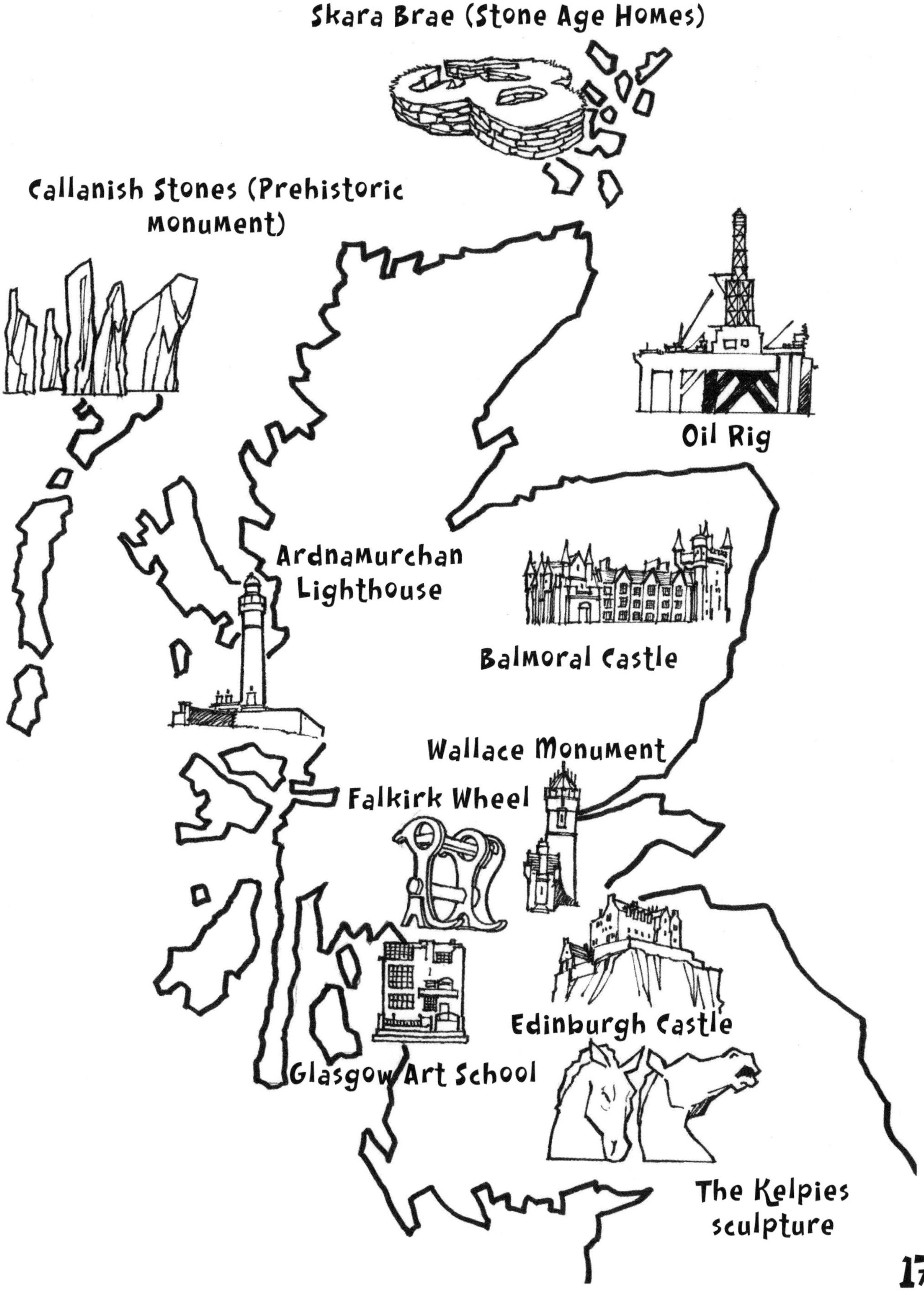

Skara Brae (Stone Age Homes)

Callanish Stones (Prehistoric Monument)

Oil Rig

Ardnamurchan Lighthouse

Balmoral Castle

Wallace Monument

Falkirk Wheel

Edinburgh Castle

Glasgow Art School

The Kelpies sculpture

Speak some Scots!

Match the English word with the Scottish word that has the same meaning.

Small

Mountain

Oh!

Church

Cheers

Lake

Yes

Now

Slàinte = _____

Och = _____

The Noo = _____

Loch = _____

Kirk = _____

Ben = _____

Wee = _____

Aye = _____

Little dog = wee dug

spot the difference

Can you spot 10 differences and
then colour in the pictures?

20

Colouring

Design your own tartan by colouring in the drawing.

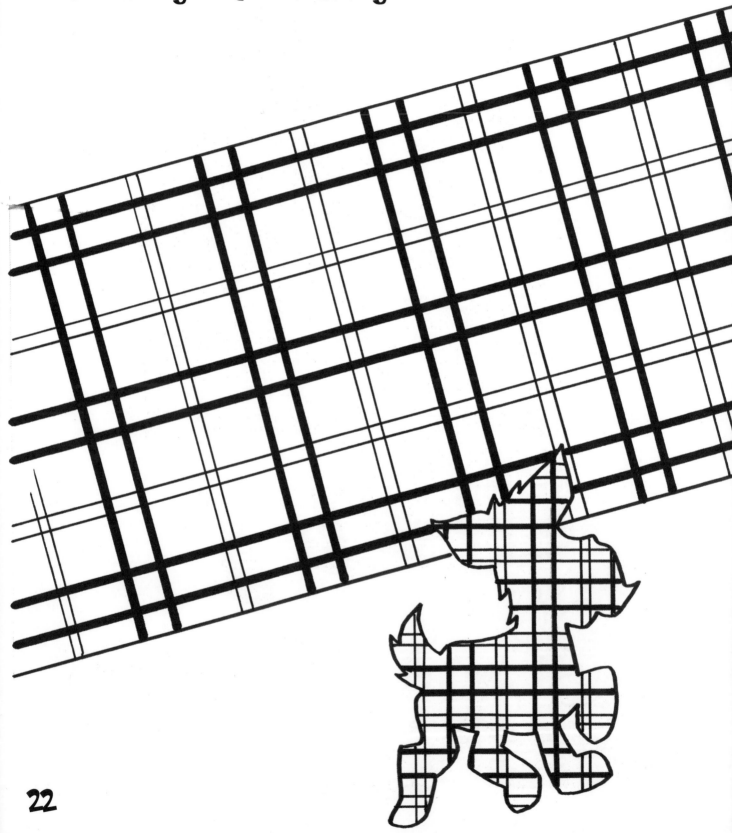

Join the dots

Can you find out who is playing the bagpipes by joining up the dots?

24

Sing along with this traditional Scottish tune...
Oh porridge thin and meagre,
Porridge thin from sowans.
Howwwwlll, howwwllll!

Porridge thin and meagre,
Porridge thin from sowans,
Porridge thin and meagre,
Porridge thin from sowans,
It is meagre and thin,
It is porridge thin from sowans.

How to draw a Highland dancer

Poetry, please!

Can you fill in the gaps in this favourite Scottish poem by Robert Burns?

Robert Burns
Romantic poet, 1759-1796

O my  L _ _ _ E's like
a red, red 🌹
_ _ _ _ S _,
That's newly sprung
(blooming) in June,
O my 💕
_ _ V _ 's like
the melodie,
That's 🍬
_ W _ _ _ T ly
play'd in 🎵🎵🎵
_ _ N _ _

Scottish sports!

Complete the pictures.

Shinty   Golf

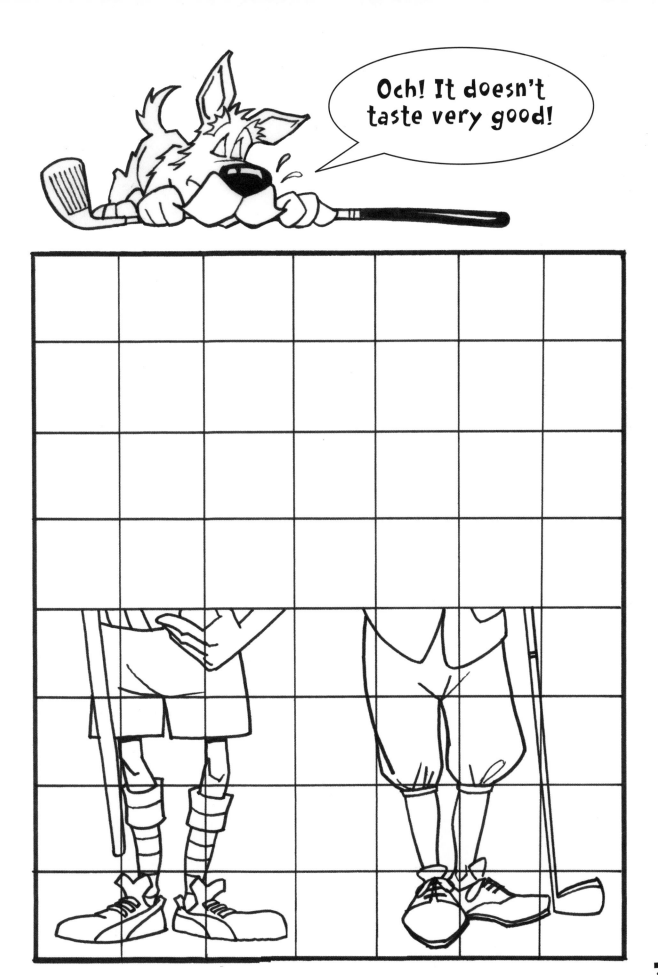

Highland games

Follow the lines to help each
competitor find what they
need for their sport.

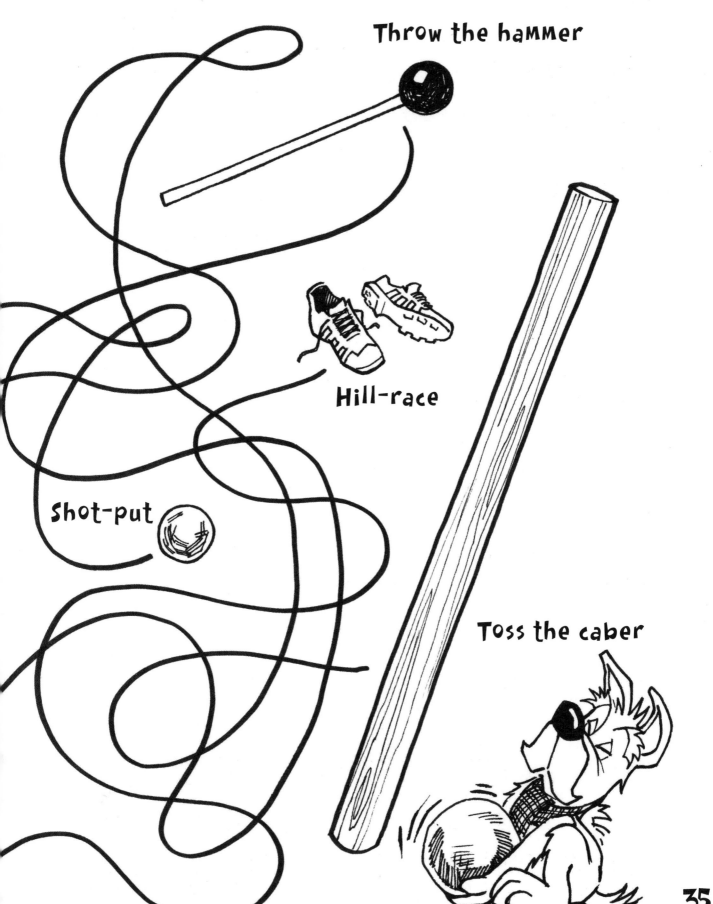

Throw the hammer

Hill-race

Shot-put

Toss the caber

35

Meet the Scottish football teams and colour them in with their team colours...

Premiership:

Aberdeen
Shirts: Red
Shorts: Red
Socks: Red

Celtic
Shirts: Green & White
Hoops, Shorts: White
Socks: White

Dundee
Shirts: Dark blue
Shorts: White
Socks: Dark blue

Dundee Utd
Shirts: Black & orange
Shorts: Black
Socks: Black & orange

Hamilton
Shirts: Red & white
Shorts: White
Socks: White

Inverness
Shirts: Blue, red stripes
Shorts: Blue
Socks: Blue & red

Kilmarnock
Shirts: Blue & white
Shorts: White
Socks: White

Motherwell
Shirts: Yellow
Shorts: Maroon
Socks: Yellow

Partick Thistle
Shirts: Yellow & orange
Shorts: Black
Socks: Orange

Ross County
Shirts: Dark blue
Shorts: Dark Blue
Socks: Dark blue & white

St Johnstone
Shirts: Light blue
Shorts: White
Socks: Light blue

St Mirren
Shirts: Black & white
Shorts: White
Socks: Black & grey

Championship:

Alloa Athletic
Shirts: Black & orange
Shorts: Black & orange
Socks: Black & orange

Cowdenbeath
Shirts: Light blue
Shorts: White
Socks: Red

Dumbarton
Shirts: White, yellow band
Shorts: White
Socks: White

Falkirk
Shirts: Dark blue
Shorts: Dark blue
Socks: Dark blue

Hearts
Shirts: Maroon
Shorts: White
Socks: Black

Hibernian
Shirts: Dark green
Shorts: White
Socks: Black

Livingston
Shirts: Yellow
Shorts: Black
Socks: Yellow

Queen of the South
Shirts: Light blue
Shorts: White
Socks: Light blue

Raith Rovers
Shirts: White
Shorts: Dark blue
Socks: White

Rangers
Shirts: Light blue
Shorts: White
Socks: Black

Look out – there's a monster about!

Join the dots to reveal the Loch Ness monster.

39

Create your own comic strip!
Colour in & add the words

Columba –
saint and
strong-Man!

Colour in these Celtic patterns!

Find the names of these Scottish monsters in the word square!

Cailleach

Old woman who brings freezing winter

Blue Men of the Minch

Attack ships and sailors

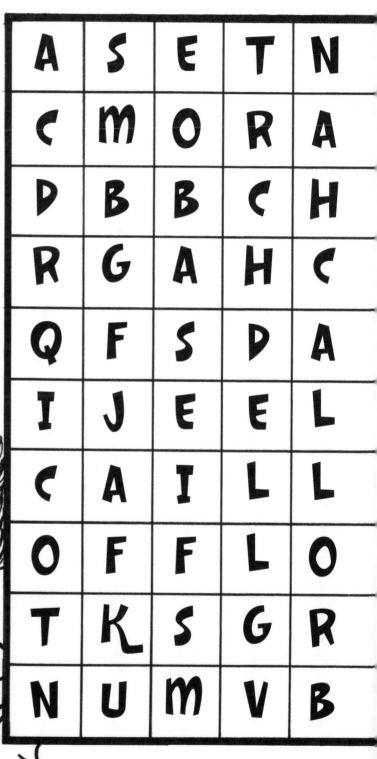

A	S	E	T	N
C	M	O	R	A
D	B	B	C	H
R	G	A	H	C
Q	F	S	D	A
I	J	E	E	L
C	A	I	L	L
O	F	F	L	O
T	K	S	G	R
N	U	M	V	B

Brollachan
Shape-shifting devourer

W	U	H	C	N
G	V	M	N	I
L	X	Z	O	M
K	Z	P	Z	E
J	P	Q	A	H
I	R	B	Y	T
E	A	C	H	F
K	E	X	D	O
H	I	C	W	N
L	U	E	M	E

Selkie
Part-woman, part-seal

Morag
Scary loch (lake) monster

Time to hide!

Haunted castle ruins

Spot the 10 differences.

Finish the drawings of these two Scottish heroes!

William Wallace

Robert the Bruce

c. 1270–1305
Led raids against
English invaders;
horribly killed.

1274–1329
Won Battle of
Bannockburn (1314)
against English, and
became Scotland's king.

Help Robert the Bruce find his spider by following the unbroken web strands:

If at first you don't succeed, try, try and try again!

Start here

51

Scottish animals

Unscramble these
Scottish animals.

LMNOSA

TRTEO

GLEEA

TNUMAONI RHAE

ERD EEDR

U O R G S E

N E I P
R T M A E N

E D R
R I R L E S U Q

L I D W   T C A

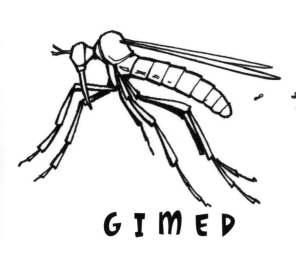

G I M E D

Count all the wild cats and one Doodle dog!

How Many eagle claws can you find?

(colour the shapes with dots)

57

Colour in this picture of a croft*

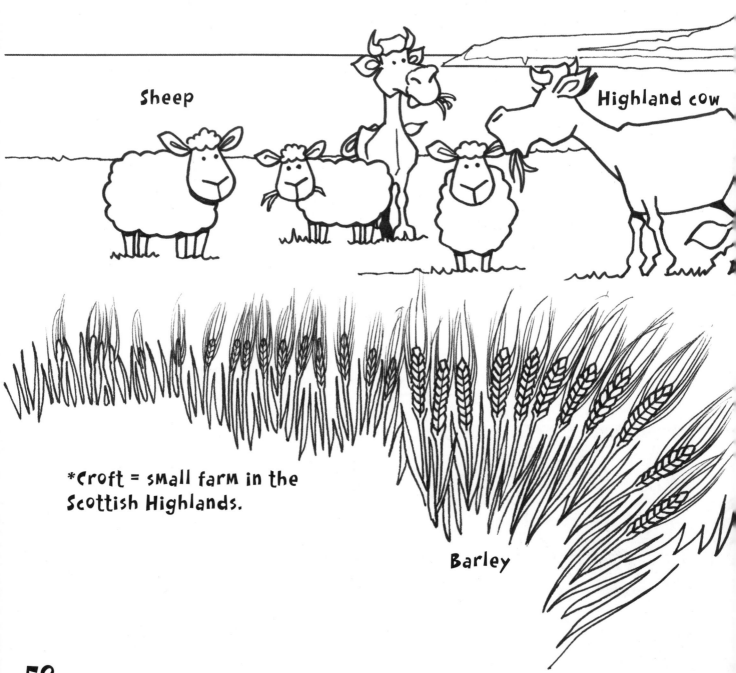

Sheep

Highland cow

*Croft = small farm in the Scottish Highlands.

Barley

58

Croft house

Steading (cow-shed)

Shetland pony

Collie = sheep dog

59

How to draw...

A Blackface Sheep

A Highland Cow

Sheep silhouette
Match the shape of the lost lamb to help it find its twin.

63

Granny's knitting

Which sheep's wool is Granny using to knit?

How to make haggis

Take one
Scottish sheep...

LUNGS

HEART

LIVER

OATMEAL
CHOPPED ONIONS
HERBS & SPICES
all cooked in the
STOMACH

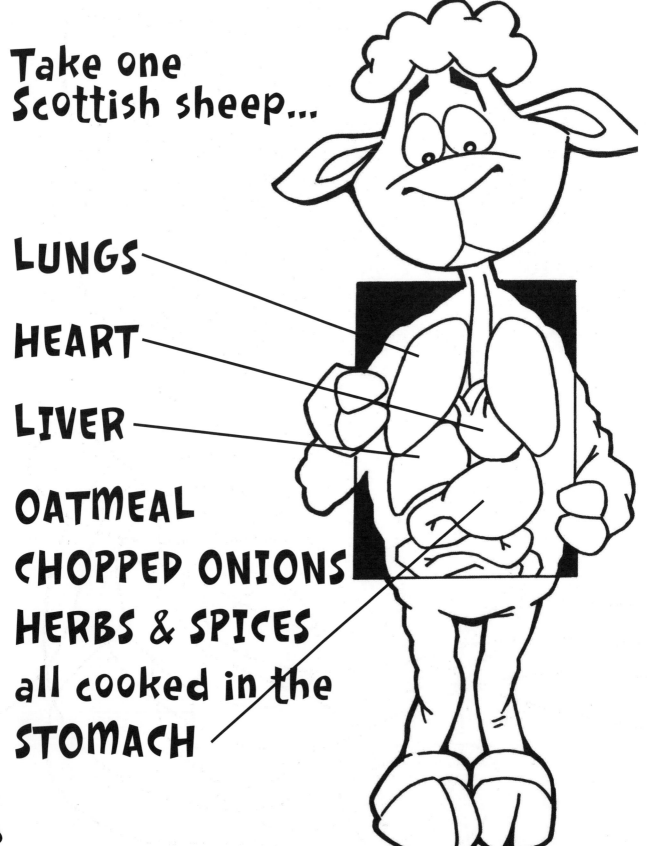

67

Sweet Scottish treats*

*Ask a grown-up to help you!

Shortbread:
You will need: 125 g butter (room temperature)
55 g caster sugar, plus a little to sprinkle
180 g plain white flour (ditto)

1. Put butter and sugar in a bowl. Beat very well until the mixture is creamy (or use an electric mixer).

2. Gently stir in the flour until it is well blended with the butter and sugar.

3. Chill the mixture in a refrigerator for about half an hour.

4. Get an adult to help you heat the oven to 170 C.

5. Sprinkle a little flour on a smooth board. Tip the mixture out of the bowl. Roll into a rectangle about 1 cm – 1.25 cm thick. Cut into 'fingers' (about 20).

6. Sprinkle the fingers with a little sugar. Gently place on metal baking tray and cook until very pale golden brown (15-20 minutes).

Fill in the Missing letters

T_BL_T

BUT_ _ _ _S _O_ _H

_ _ _ _I _ _UR _H

_O_K

_ _ _N_EE_AK_

Out at sea

Can you match the shapes of these creatures?

Basking shark

Seal

Dolphin

Puffin

Minke Whale

Crab

Orca

Gannet

Whelk

Mussel

Tern

Scottish seashore villains!

Sawney Bean – wrecker and cannibal (Lived around 1500)

William Kidd - pirate (lived 1645-1701)

Gone fishing

Unscramble the names and count how many of each fish are in the net.

ODC

RECLAEMK

KTSAE

RERNGIH

Splendid Scottish ships!

Scottish ships and shipbuilders are famous worldwide.

Match the ships with their shapes.

CHARLOTTE DUNDAS (1803)

CUTTY SARK (1869)

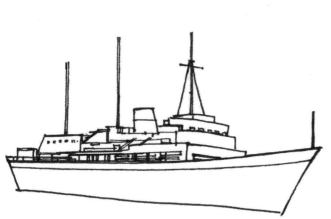

DISCOVERY (1901)

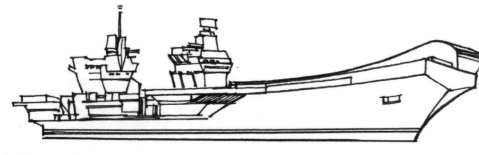

BRITANNIA (1953)

HMS QUEEN ELIZABETH (2014)

QUEEN ELIZABETH 2 (1967)

How to draw a lifeboat!

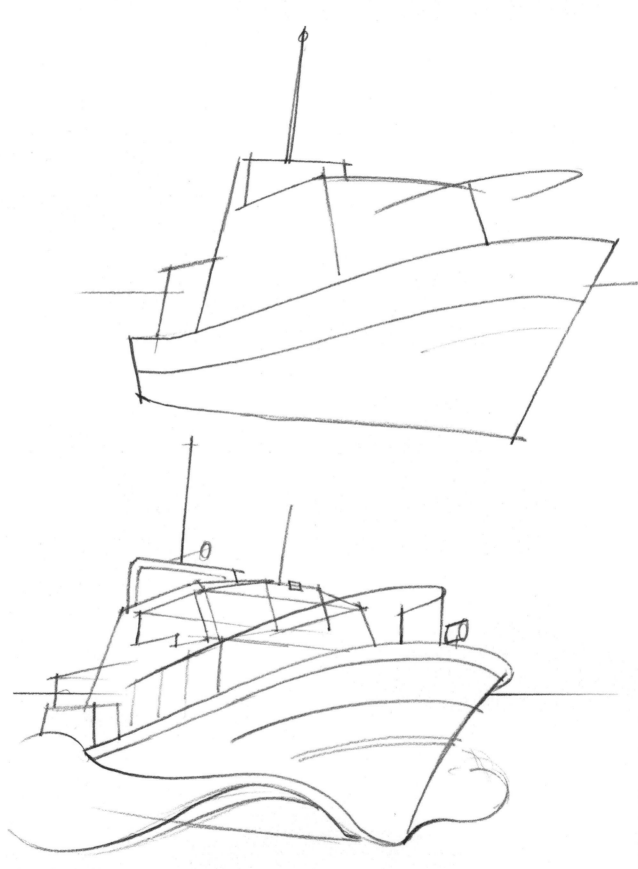

GREAT SCOTS! Engineers and inventors

Unjumble the inventions or discoveries and match each one with its inventor.

80

Alexander Graham Bell
(1847-1922)

EOEPETLHN

Robert Watson-Watt
(1892-1973)

AARDR

John Logie Baird
(1888-1946)

NTEELOVSII

James Clerk Maxwell
(1831-1879)

IORDA

Alexander Fleming
(1881-1955)

LLIICINEPN

William Cullen
(1710-1790)

GIRAERTFEORR

Create your own pattern

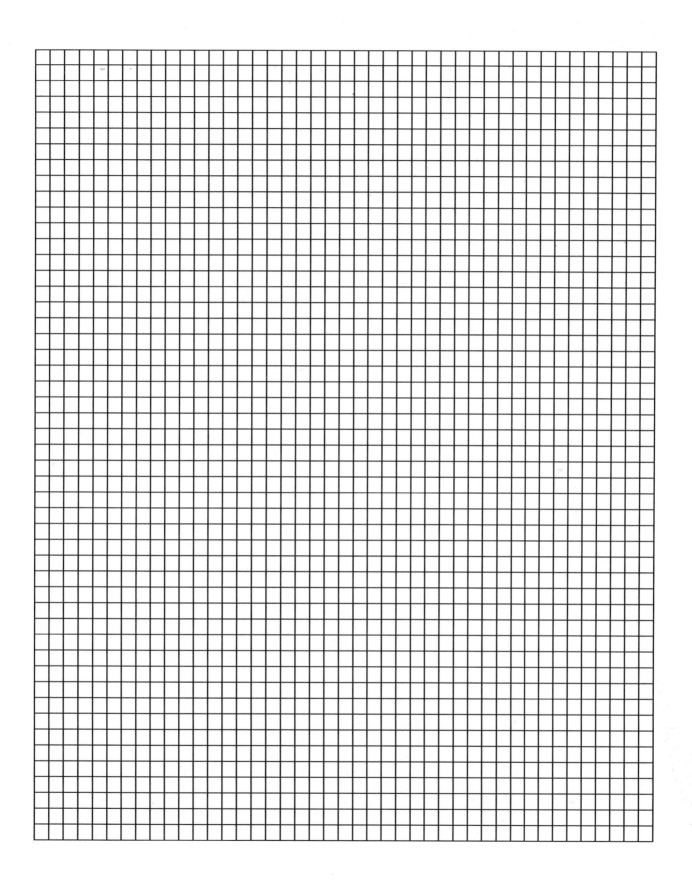

Black gold!*

Find the two oil rigs that exactly match the one below.

*Oil

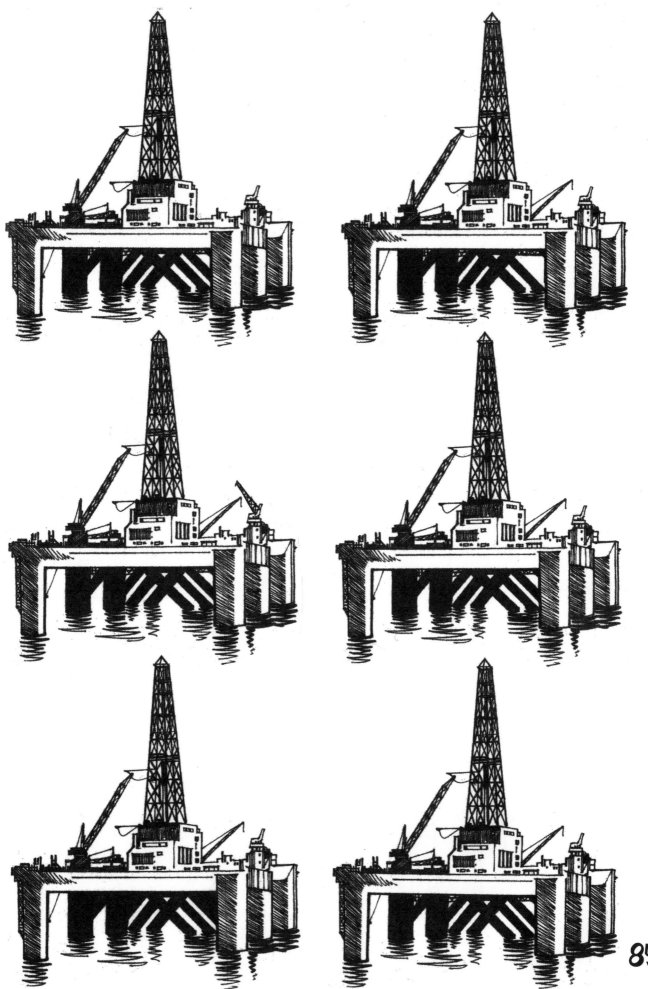

85

Tumbling turbines

Pick up the fallen wind turbines in the right order – starting with the one on top!

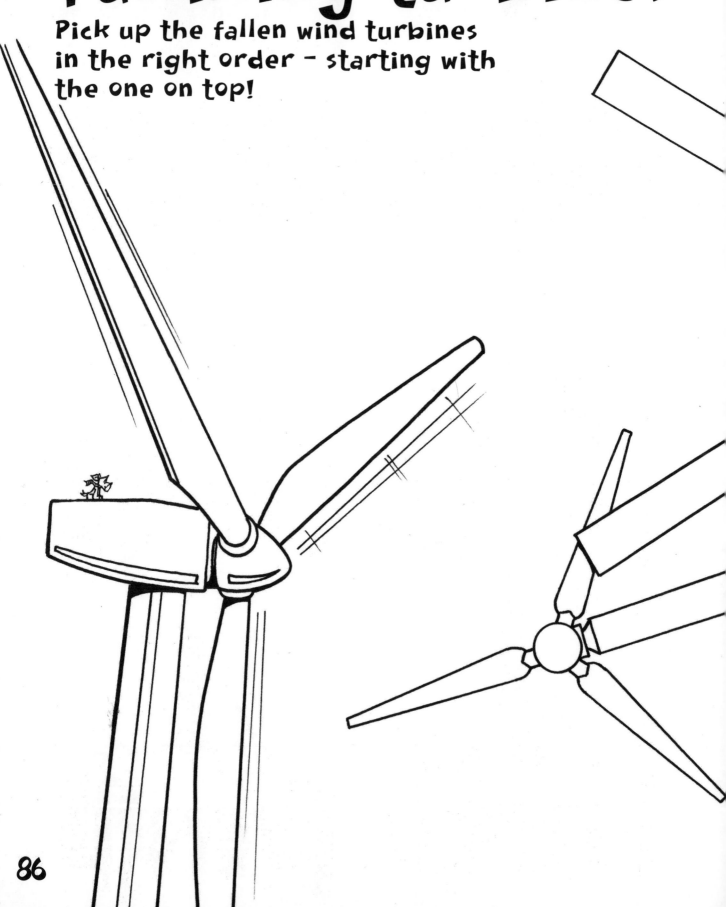

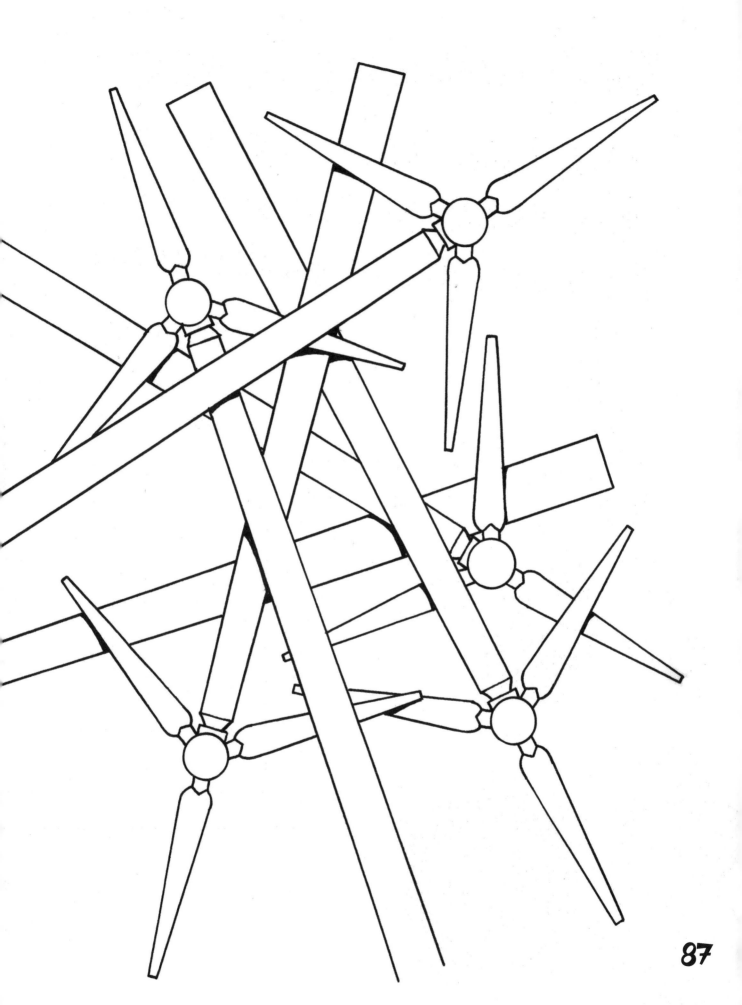

87

Parliament Maze

Go over and under on the road to the Scottish Parliament, in Edinburgh.

89

Great Scots today

DYAN RUMYAR

LIYBL NONYLOCL

XLAE DNLMOAS

RIS NESA NOERYCN

KJ WLRNIOG

RSI RHISC YHO

Answers

Pages 8-9:

Pages 10-11: 1 - Ben Nevis, 2 - Old Man of Hoy, 3 - Loch Lomond, 4 - River Clyde, 5 - Arthur's Seat, 6 - Cairngorms, 7 - Loch Ness, 8 - Fingal's Cave, 9 - Rannoch Moor

Pages 12-13:

Pages 14-15:

Pages 16-17:

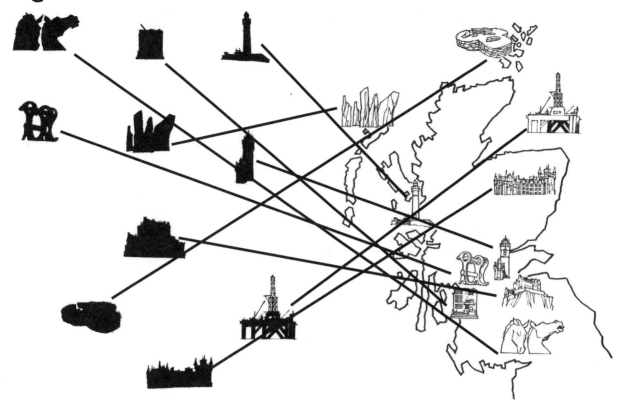

Pages 18-19: Slàinte = Cheers, Och = Oh!,
The Noo = Now, Loch = Lake, Kirk = Church,
Ben = Mountain, Wee = Small, Aye = Yes

Pages 30-31: O my love's like a red, red rose, That's newly sprung in June; O my love's like the melodie, That's sweetly played in tune.

Pages 20-21:

Pages 44-45:

A	S	E	T	N	W	U	H	C	N
C	M	O	R	A	G	V	M	N	I
D	B	B	C	H	L	X	Z	O	M
R	G	A	H	C	K	Z	P	Z	E
Q	F	S	P	A	J	P	Q	A	H
I	J	E	E	L	I	R	B	Y	T
C	A	I	L	L	E	A	C	H	F
O	F	F	L	O	K	E	X	D	O
T	K	S	G	R	H	I	C	W	N
N	U	M	V	B	L	U	E	M	E

Pages 46-47:

Pages 50-51:

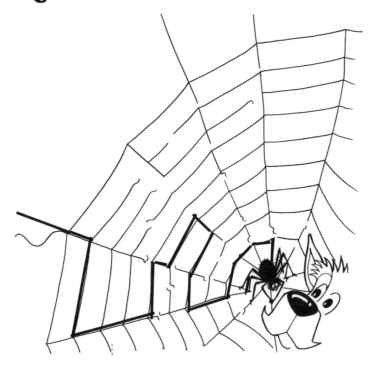

Pages 52-53:

LMNOSA = SALMON

TRTEO = OTTER

GLEEA = EAGLE

TNUMAONI RHAE = MOUNTAIN HARE

ERD EEDR = RED DEER

UORGSE = GROUSE

NEIP RTMAEN = PINE MARTEN

EDR RIRLESUQ = RED SQUIRREL

LIDW TCA = WILD CAT

GIMED = MIDGE

Pages 54-55: There are 18 wild cats.

Pages 56-57: There are 7 claws.

Pages 62-63: The matching shape is top centre.

Pages 68-69: Tablet, Butterscotch, Edinburgh Rock, Dundee Cake.

Pages 70-71:

# Pages 74-75:
Cod = 10, Mackerel = 13, Skate = 7, Herring = 18

Pages 76-77:

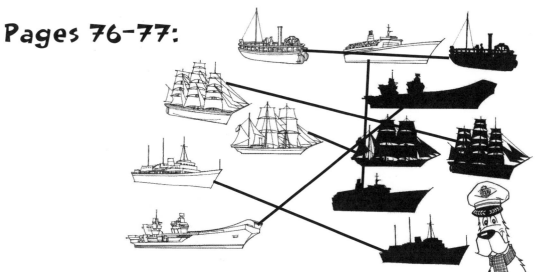

Pages 80-81:

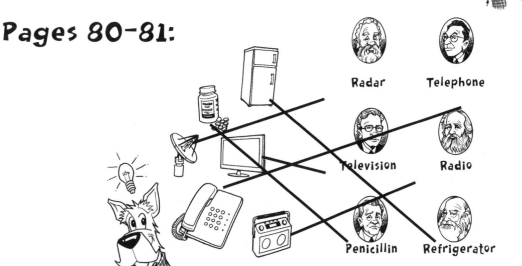

Radar   Telephone

Television   Radio

Penicillin   Refrigerator

Pages 84-85: The centre right and bottom right rigs are the same.

Pages 86-87:

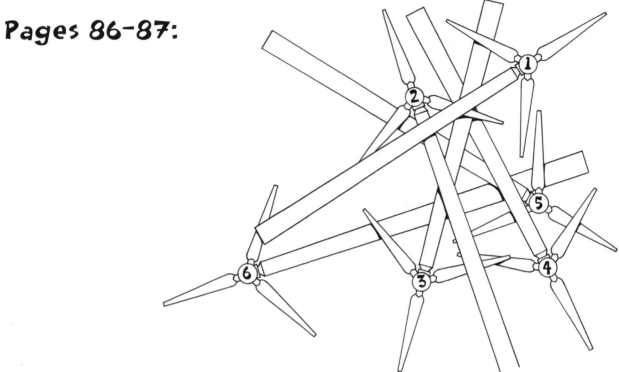

Pages 88-89:

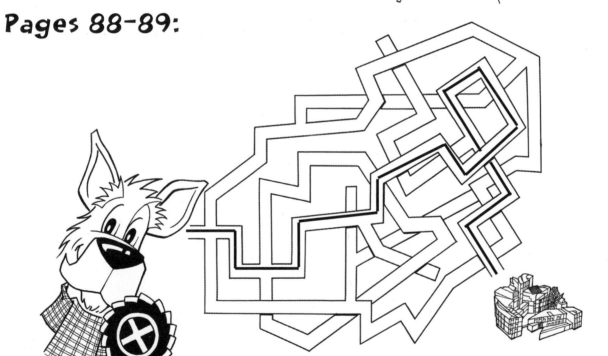

Pages 90-91: LIBYL NONYLOCL = Billy Connolly, DYAN RUMYAR = Andy Murray, XLAE DNLMOAS = Alex Salmond, KJ WLRNIOG = JK Rowling, RIS NESA NOERCYN = Sir Sean Connery, RSI RHISC YHO = Sir Chris Hoy